Monkey Puz

One of these monkeys has stolen the Pearl o
Can you work out which one from the clues below?

• It has a curly tail •

• It has three bananas • It has a cheeky grin •

Tablet Wordsearch

Professor Penny has found this mysterious stone tablet in the depths of the rainforest. Find the hidden words for everything she'll need on her trip.

· COMPASS · ROPE · MONKEY · CAMEL ·
· HAT · MACHETTE · HORSE · BOTTLE ·

M	C	A	Y	E	K	N	O	M
E	A	O	B	G	R	M	E	E
S	H	C	O	M	P	A	S	S
R	T	Q	H	O	P	J	U	P
O	L	C	E	E	N	H	G	H
H	D	P	R	P	T	U	O	A
Y	O	R	E	U	I	T	T	T
R	O	B	O	T	T	L	E	B
T	C	A	M	E	L	U	L	A

The words could be hiding in any direction, even back-to-front!

Face to Face

These two old pals haven't seen each other in a long time!
Study the pictures then try to spot nine differences
between the scenes.

Amazing Volcanoes

Create a volcanic eruption complete with oozing lava!

You will need: A clear plastic bottle · Scissors · Plasticine · Paper · Felt-tip pens · Vinegar · Washing-up liquid · Red food colouring · Baking powder ·

! ASK AN ADULT TO HELP YOU.

1 Ask an adult to help you cut the bottle in half and discard the bottom section.

2 Snip 2 cm off the top to create a 'magma chamber'. Turn this piece upside-down and put it back inside the bottle.

3 Seal the edge of your 'magma chamber' with some Plasticine.

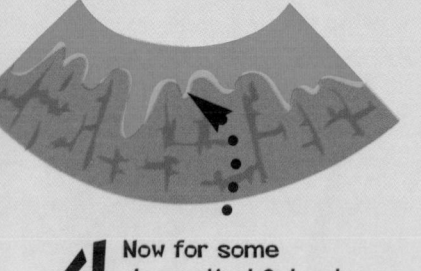

4 Now for some decoration! Cut out a collar of paper and colour it to look like an exploding volcano.

5 Push the volcano collar up inside the cone of the bottle.

7 Spoon two teaspoons of baking powder into the volcano's crater.

8 It's time for an eruption! Slowly pour your lava mixture into the crater, then wait for the volcano to blow! (It's probably best to do this bit outside!)

6 To make the lava, mix together 150 ml vinegar, three tablespoons of washing-up liquid and two drops of food colouring.

"Yikes!"

You can re-charge your volcano again and again. Just rinse out the magma chamber and add another batch of ingredients!

Carpet Caper

Which of these flying carpets will reach the magical
floating castle and which will disappear
into the clouds?

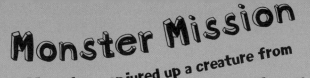

Monster Mission

Maisy has conjured up a creature from spare parts she found in the spell room. Design your own monster below.

Friend or Fiend?

This wizard has conjured up a fiery companion.
Join the dots to find out if he'll be pleased to see it.

Crocodile Creek

Annie is trying to cross the river without getting eaten!
Can you spot seven differences
between these two pictures?

a

b

Papier-mâché Mobile

Up, up and away! Philippa Fogg is taking to the skies!
Decorate your room with this marvellous balloon mobile.

You will need: Balloon · Cardboard tube · Sticky tape · Old bowl · · Old newspapers · PVA glue · Paintbrush · Yoghurt pot · · Hole punch · Wool or string · Paints · Scissors · Ruler ·

1 Blow up the balloon and tie the end. Use sticky tape to secure your balloon to the cardboard tube.

2 Tear the newspaper into strips. Mix the PVA glue with a little water in a bowl.

3 Dip the strips into the glue mix one by one, then criss-cross them over your balloon.

4 Carefully cover the balloon several times with the strips. Try to keep the layers of paper the same thickness all over.

5 Leave your balloon to dry in a safe place overnight.

6 While it dries, make the basket. Take the yoghurt pot and ask an adult to help punch four holes in the top rim as shown.

8 Once your balloon is dry you can paint it!

7 Make a long plait from wool and glue it around the pot to make it look like a proper basket.

9 Pop the balloon and remove it from inside the papier-mâché shell. Neatly trim the edges along the bottom.

10 Cut four, 20cm lengths of wool and knot them through the holes of your basket. Then punch four holes in the balloon and knot the other ends of the wool through them.

Chocks away!

Ocean Pairs

Help these undersea creatures find their missing mates.

Professor's Wordsearch

When the professor was shipwrecked on Smuggler's Island, he couldn't believe his luck!

The jungle is buzzing with exotic plants and animals. Study the word grid carefully, then draw a line through the nine specimens he's found.

- BANANA · PALM ·
- COCONUT · MONKEY ·
- PARROT · TARANTULA ·
- LEOPARD · LEMUR · BEETLE ·

X	C	A	P	A	L	M	L	L
M	B	O	B	G	R	M	E	E
O	H	A	C	W	N	S	M	O
N	T	Q	N	O	P	J	U	P
K	L	C	Y	A	N	F	R	A
E	D	V	R	P	N	U	O	R
Y	W	R	E	U	I	A	T	D
Z	O	K	E	L	T	E	E	B
T	A	R	A	N	T	U	L	A

Professor's top tip
The words could be hiding in any direction, even backwards.

Tomb Terror!

Clever Clarissa has stumbled across something
in the dark! Join up the dots if you dare...

Which is Wilbur?

Amazing Maisy has turned her friends into frogs and now she can't remember who is who. Help her find Wilbur from the statements below.

a

b

c

- He wears striped trousers.
- He wears glasses.
- He doesn't have a bow tie.

Perfect Potions

Mouth-watering magical mixtures to conjure up!

Before you get started, collect:

⚠️ ASK AN ADULT TO HELP YOU.

· Medium saucepan · Measuring jug · Wooden spoon ·
· Kitchen scales · Knife · Lemon squeezer · Sieve · Large jug ·

Wizard's Chocolate Warmer
For four servings you will need:
· 125ml water
· 60g chocolate
· 750ml milk
· Pinch of salt
· 1 tsp of dried cinnamon

1 Break the chocolate into small chunks and place in a saucepan.

2 Add the water and stir over a medium heat until the chocolate melts.

3 Bring to the boil and simmer for 2 minutes then turn the heat down low.

4 Stir in the milk and add the pinch of salt to help it thicken.

5 Add the cinnamon and heat for 5 minutes more until thoroughly warmed through. Check it's not too hot before you pour yourself a big mug.

Oops, I've turned into a frog!

ASK AN ADULT TO HELP YOU.

Sorcerer's Lemon Spritzer
For four servings you will need:

- 150g sugar
- Juice of 4 lemons
- 750ml water, plus extra to taste

1 Put the sugar and water in a saucepan. Stir over a low heat until the sugar dissolves.

2 Once the sugar has dissolved, bring to the boil. Simmer for 2 minutes.

3 Add the lemon juice and stir well, then leave to cool for half an hour.

4 Sieve the mixture over the jug to remove all the bits. Finally, add extra water to taste and to help to cool the spritzer.

Animal Anagrams

There's trouble at the ranch! Unscramble the letters to corral these animals back into their pens.

1. . . . .

SE RO H

2. . . . .

TO AG

K CENC IH

3. . . . .

RE YKU T

FAL OBUF

4. . . . .

5. . . . .

Treasure Hunt

It's rumoured that an old sea captain has hidden his bounty in these parts – can you find it? Find the missing picture stickers to complete this old scroll. **Happy hunting!**

Check your   , then walk five paces east. Walk past the   then cross the   . Under the next   use your   to dig a big hole.

When you find the   use the   to unlock it.

Inside you will find the   .

Ship to Shore

Which of these lucky sailors will manage to row to the safety of his own private desert island?

A sticky fate in the ocean deep is waiting for the other two!

Wizard's Crossword

Complete the crossword using the pictures as clues.

Cutting to the Aces

This sharp card trick will astound your friends and family! Ask someone to split a deck into four piles. Wait for the gasps when you reveal that each stack is topped with an ace!

You will need: A standard pack of playing cards

1 Before performing the trick, prepare the cards by putting all the aces on the top of the pack. When you're ready to start, make a show of shuffling the deck, carefully keeping the aces on top.

2 Ask a friend to divide the deck into four roughly equal sections, holding the cards face down the whole time. Make a mental note of which pile has the aces on top.

aces

3 Tell your friend to pick up one of the piles that doesn't have the aces. Keeping the cards face down, ask them to remove three cards from the top and put them on the bottom.

4 Now ask your friend to take three cards from the top of the same pile and place one on top of each of the three remaining piles.

5 Next, request that your friend repeats steps 3 and 4 with the other two piles that don't hold the aces.

6 When they're ready, ask your friend to go through the same process with the pile that holds the aces.

7 Finally, ask your friend to put all four piles of cards back on the table. Turn over the top card of each pile with a few magic words and a flourish. Each one will be topped with an ace!

"Mystifying!"

Quick on the Draw

Now you're a master magician, give this trick a try...

1 Ask a friend to pick a card from the pack and memorise it. Shuffle the cards, then tell your friend to place the chosen card on the top of the deck.

2 Hold the cards behind your back and secretly turn the top card over so that it faces upwards.

3 Now bring the cards back in front of you with the back of the deck facing your friend. The card you turned over a moment ago will now be facing you!

4 Memorise your friend's card, then put the pack behind your back again. Secretly turn the card over and place it anywhere in the deck.

5 Smile mysteriously, then bring the cards to the front and give them a good shuffle. When you get to the chosen card, hold it up in the air!

Dinner is Served!

The ship's cook has been busy in the galley!
Can you spot eight differences between these two pictures?

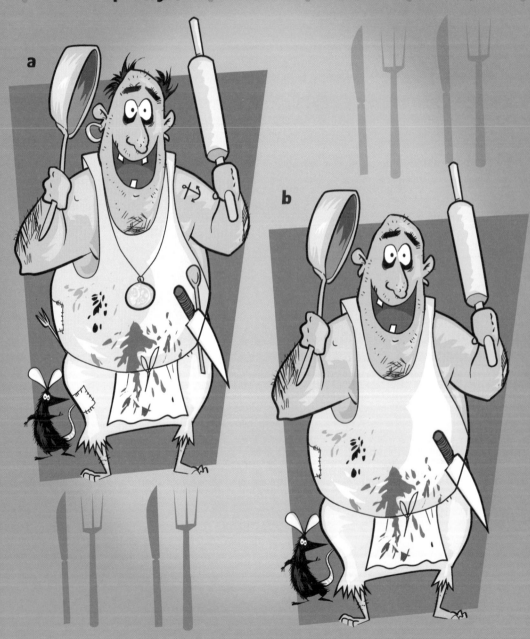

a

b

Magical Mess-up

Oh dear! Everything has disappeared with a big POP!
Study the image for a minute, then cover it up and
see if you can answer the questions at the bottom.

1. What colour is the handkerchief?
2. How many rings are there?
3. What shape is on top of the box?
4. What is to the right of the rabbit?

Desert Camel Race

Which of the three explorers will reach the lost city of Isthea?

Jungle Jumble

There's trouble in the jungle – the animals
have forgotten how to spell their names!
Help them out by unscrambling the letters below.

1. . . . .
ONLI

2. . . . .
EYNMOK

3. . . . .
ILECCOROD

5. . . . .
ETRIG

4. . . . .
ELMCA

Rocky Road Chews

All cowboys and cowgirls need something to munch on when they're out in the desert.

You will need: Plastic food wrap · Baking tray · Plastic bag · · Rolling pin · Kitchen scales · Saucepan · Wooden spoon ·

Makes about 16 totally chewy squares!

ASK AN ADULT TO HELP YOU.

Ingredients

* 200 g plain chocolate
* 150 g milk chocolate
* 4 tbsp golden syrup
* 150 g butter
* 175 g Rich Tea biscuits
* 150 g chopped brazil nuts
* 150 g chopped marshmallows

BE ALLERGY AWARE!
If you are allergic to brazil nuts, replace them with stoned cherries, dried fruit or crisp rice cereal!

1 Line the baking tray with plastic food wrap, then put it to one side.

2 Tip the biscuits into a plastic bag and push the air out. Tie a knot in the top, then crush the bag with a rolling pin.

3 Ask an adult to help you to gently melt the chocolate, syrup and butter in a pan.

4 Take the saucepan off the heat and stir in the crushed biscuits.

6 Spread the rocky road mix onto the prepared baking tray then pop it in the fridge to cool.

5 Pour the nuts and chopped marshmallows into the pan and quickly mix it all together.

7 When the tray is fully chilled, cut the rocky road into chunky squares.

Gorgeous Goblins

Eric and Cedric are twin goblins, but they're not identical.
Study the pictures and find seven differences between
the two brothers.

Eric

Cedric

Answers

Monkey Puzzle

c

Tablet Wordsearch

Face to Face

Carpet Caper

b

Crocodile Creek

Ocean Pairs

Professor's Wordsearch

X	C	A	P	A	L	M	L	L
M	B	O	B	G	R	M	E	E
O	H	A	C	W	N	S	M	O
N	T	Q	N	O	P	J	U	P
K	L	C	Y	A	N	F	R	A
E	D	V	R	P	N	W	U	O	R
Y	W	R	E	U	I	A	T	D
Z	O	K	E	L	T	E	E	B
T	A	R	A	N	T	U	L	A

Which is Wilbur?
a

Treasure Hunt

Check your <u>compass</u>, then walk five paces east. Walk past the <u>palm tree</u> then cross the <u>bridge</u>. Under the next <u>palm tree</u> use your <u>spade</u> to dig a big hole. When you find the <u>chest</u> use the <u>key</u> to unlock it. Inside you will find the <u>treasure</u>.

Ship to Shore
c

Wizard's Crossword

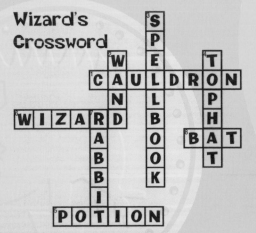

Dinner is Served!

1. His hair is missing.
2. His earring is missing.
3. He only has two teeth instead of three.
4. The wooden spoon is missing.
5. The fork is missing.
6. The patch is missing from his breeches.
7. His medallion is missing.
8. His anchor tattoo is missing.

Desert Camel Race
b

Jungle Jumble

1. Lion
2. Monkey
3. Crocodile
4. Tiger
5. Camel

Gorgeous Goblins

Gorgeous Goblins

Eric and Cedric are twin goblins, but they're not identical. Study the pictures and find seven differences between the two brothers.

Eric

Cedric

13